Fragments of Creation

BEYOND THE VEIL OF TIME

DEYSI FAETH

Illustrations by Mukti Bird

PALMETTO
PUBLISHING
Charleston, SC
www.PalmettoPublishing.com

Hardcover ISBN: 979-8-8229-3077-3
Paperback ISBN: 979-8-8229-3078-0
eBook ISBN: 979-8-8229-4558-6

Fragments
of Creation

To Thy Self Remembering

Contents

Foreword by Mukti Bird

This is not your usual book. This is a collection of living stories. They are alive because they are a part of each one of us. Each story is a parable, brimming with wisdom and an experience of transcendence that at one point I feel each human heart will face. While the main character of this book is female, her perspective is universal and beyond gender. She is courageous and vulnerable, like a hawk ready to take flight and also a fledgling learning from her mother.

This book is an unraveling of what it means to be alive in this time, what it is to be human and face all of our emotions—all our pain, our joy, the lessons that come and go like familiar faces or unexpected seasons of change and growth. These stories are unique in their nature, they are innocent yet intricate. Because they tell the story of a soul walking through many lifetimes and experiences, it is a nonlinear narrative. You could open to any chapter and find what your heart needs to hear in this moment.

Working on these illustrations for nearly a year, I have sat with each story, contemplating and reflecting, savoring it like a warm pot of tea. Each story lesson I sit with deeply mirrors a current insight in my life. I have found this incredibly magical and supportive, a sort of testimony to the timelessness of these parables. I hope it can serve you in the same way.

We are not alone here on earth, nor are we meant to be alone. Storytelling is another means of bridging and connecting the spirit within us that is one. Although each of our life experiences is unique and our own, we walk together and reflect each other, and I find this book is in support of this courage to walk with faith in a time of seeming darkness, to find and know that eternal light within.

To understand something deeper calls us home to ourselves. Deysi's stories encourage us to meet and accept ourselves as we are in this moment. One minute, we are flying through light; the next, a cat is showing us the path in a dense forest, smiling with its eyes. Suddenly an angel asks us if we really want to choose this life, and a warrior finds her voice and strength. We throw our burdens into a roaring fire, surrender, and release in the rain of our own tears, as a wise elephant takes us through the desert, and we hold ourselves in the palm of our hand. This is a taste of the river of imagery you will find yourself passing through while reading this book and taking in each fragment.

Fragments of Creation is an invitation into the mystery of the inner realms of our hearts. This is not a mystery to be solved but an opportunity to contemplate, reflect, and find our own reverence and strength in this fabric of existence—a broad inner perspective of our heroine, magically weaved throughout these stories.

All my love,
Mukti

Introduction

What if you could access all your memories from every life lived and every timeline possible? This could all be very overwhelming without a proper filter. Perhaps this is why we are born with forgetfulness, for if we were inundated with such large quantities of information, would we really be able to be present here on earth or even really live?

Although there is a suffering we endure because of this forgetfulness, it does not come without purpose. We all know the feeling of being lost, afraid, uncertain, or confused about where we "should" go or who we "could" be and praying for guidance. Many of us are filled with visions of possibilities of our lives often without any concept of how to get there. We may think that life is a journey from A to Z, yet forget all the letters that come in between, with some being consonants and some being vowels.

It's not about the destination; it's about the journey.

How often are we able to see and witness every step along the way and, in addition, embrace each layer of experience without judgment or condemnation? What if we could embody all parts of us, even the ones that cause us to struggle and challenge us? What would happen if we could face all experiences and welcome them into wholeness? Can you imagine what this could feel like? For most, it may be safe to say that feeling would be bliss. A place of true remembrance—of wholeness, peace, stillness, and grace.

Life holds universal lessons and emotions, and we all meet those in very unique ways. Yet there is a shared quality beneath them, which is how we can relate to one another and through which we connect on a deeper plane. Each story in this book is a doorway for reconciliation, and reading the words is the key to opening the inner realms of the soul and remembering. They are the stories of the Maiden and the coming of age dealing with the ancestral and karmic imprints upon the body, mind, and soul—a mythic mapping of the journey along the way.

When I was a young child, my emotions were often my enemies, a hindrance to my being and way. When I felt something, I felt it deeply, and it often overtook any sense of control. I ran from them for many years, trying to numb their presence. The writing of these stories was my willingness to face them. They were my chance to stop hiding from myself and learn to listen. And most importantly, they were the lesson that sometimes you just have to let it *RAIN*.

To let it RAIN is to *recognize* what state of mind or emotion you are witnessing, *accept* it as it is, *investigate* by asking questions about its purpose or message, and eventually practice *non identification* with that experience. You are not your body; you are not your mind or emotions. Through this process, one can learn self-mastery and over-come hindrances.

This concept comes from a Ted Talk I viewed years ago, where a Shaolin Master shared a story, a story about self-mastery and the five hindrances we meet along the way that keep us from "climbing the mountain."[1] The mountain is a metaphor for the seeking of clarity—for the view and perspective that comes when one sits at the "peak."

---

1   TEDxVitosha. *Master Shi Heng Yi—5 Hindrances to Self-Mastery*. YouTube, 13 Feb. 2020, https://www.youtube.com/watch?v=4-079YIasck. Accessed Mar. 2020.

Each person's view from the top of the mountain is very different from everyone else's; everyone's journey up the mountain takes a very different path. And some choose not to climb the mountain at all because of these five hindrances. After explaining the blocks and distractions we face along the way, he offers a very simple solution: when you meet the "dark clouds" on your journey up the mountain, instead of stopping or seeking shelter (distractions), just let it RAIN.

> All of our lifetimes, all of our lives are too unique to copy the path from someone else. To bring meaning to your life, to bring purpose into your life, you need to learn and master yourself, and don't let the hindrances stop you.
> —Master Shi Heng Yi

This video resonated with such profound insight that I immediately took it to heart. As I am a Capricorn north node, climbing the mountain is very much a part of my directive. And rain being the most soothing sound upon my soul, I knew this Ted Talk was talking directly to me. Through its lessons, I found myself determined to climb my mountain, to seek clarity, and to witness my whole self, which included facing all the hindrances along the way.

And so, these stories are just that: the reconciliation of the pieces of my own soul, which mirror the fragments of creation itself. Like the facets of a crystal, each window is a peek into the beauty of the whole. Each reflects the color and light of the crystal's energy. Similar to the Major Arcana in the Tarot, each is a snippet of the Fool's journey.

There is no right or wrong way to read these stories. You may use them as meditative journeys or contemplations, as in Lectio Divina—the practice of reading sacred stories, meditating on their messages and meanings, and responding to and resting in that experience. You may use them as you would an oracle, or as simply something to relate to. They can be read through from beginning to end or just opened to a random one when you feel prompted.

Through these portals, you are invited to ponder their messages, respond with your own experiences, and discover the universal wisdom of life hidden within.

Sat Nam,

Deysi Faeth

Through this door, you get to choose who you want to be:
a creature of the land, sky, or sea.
This door is an emblem for the power of choice.
Realities overlap here on the brink of death;
death is but a transition from this to that.
Hold the vision of your truth,
buried deep within your heart,
then open the door to the life you wish to lead.

Prologue: The Journey of Being Reborn

"Are you sure you want to choose this life?" the angel asked. "There are others to choose from."

"Yes, I am sure," the girl responded confidently.

The angel continued her inquiry, "Do you understand these lessons of your past?"

The girl paused for but a moment. "Yes, I understand," she replied firmly.

The angel motioned down toward the edge of the platform where they stood. "Then why choose this path?"

"Because I would do it again," the girl stated somberly. Without further hesitation, she jumped forth from the cloudy ledge. Her spirit rushed toward the watery planet below, following the threads of her contract, to find herself once more in the land of the living.

The girl knew what she signed up for. The life she chose would hold hard lessons for her to overcome. She needed these obstacles, though, to learn the qualities required for her soul's true path. In the world she would enter, she knew she would experience its suffering. Last time she was there, she lashed out and sought revenge on those who wished her ill. She knew why she reacted in such a way then, and now she knew why it had only brought more pain. And more than anything, she knew that if she were faced with the same circumstances, she would do it again. She had not learned what she desired.

And so, the girl prayed. *This time would be different—it had to be different.* This time, she would not only have the strength to stand up for herself but use that strength wisely and with tender care in the ongoing battle for peace and equality. The word *tender* singed her like an open flame. She did not enjoy the feeling of softness, but she would learn to appreciate its teaching—this world had enough aggression, and this time, she would channel her rage in a different way. Not as pure destruction, but as a rebirthing.

However, time on this planet passed. Promises of before were forgotten, lost in transition. Challenges were met, and distractions led her off her chosen path. Now beyond the road she had paved for herself, she found herself lost deep in the thickets.

While wandering these woods, the girl happened upon a cat, apparently indulging in a midday nap. As the girl approached this resting feline, the cat rustled with this interruption to its surroundings. It stood and stretched. Then it asked the girl with a yawn, "Have you come from the road over there?"

"What road?" she asked, alarmed, looking around. "I don't remember a road." The girl tried to think back to where she came from, yet her memories all seemed to blur. *Was I on a road before now?* she wondered silently, or did she just say that out loud?

"Well, it's not very far from here. How long have you been wandering about?" The cat began to lick its paws, half interested.

"For as long I can remember," the girl said as she furrowed her eyebrows. "I am not sure exactly; it all seems like a distant dream." She concentrated deeply to connect the dots of her recent journey.

"Don't you think it's time to wake up?" the cat asked simply.

The girl immediately shook her head wildly. "Why? I like it here," she responded. "It's quiet."

"Are you sure about that?" asked the cat flippantly.

At first the girl wanted to speak with immediate affirmation, but a little voice inside told her to listen. The girl closed her eyes—she heard the rustling of fallen leaves, the buzzing of insects, the rumbling of a nearby stream, and the creaking of ancient trees. Yet these sounds did not come one by one, but all at once like a wave crashing onto the shore of her mind.

She stood there dazed, lost in the cacophony of noise, trying to trace all the sounds back to their sources until the cat rubbed itself upon her legs. The girl looked down to where the feline stood. "Ah, sorry, I forgot you were here." She looked around again. "I forgot where I was."

"No matter to me," said the cat. "The matter for you is do you wish to stay lost?"

The girl shrugged. "I guess not."

"You guess?" said the cat, with intrigue and surprise in its voice.

"Well...I don't really remember what it is like to not be lost."

"I see." The cat sat rightly, bearing its chest and curling its tail around its body. "Then why not find your way back to the road and decide then?" it asked with a dare in its eyes.

Unsure of which direction to go, the girl asked, "Will you guide me?"

With a gesture of its head, the cat motioned to an opening in the trees. "There is a shortcut over there; the owl told me so. Follow me."

The girl scanned the greenery to find this owl the cat spoke of. Her feet began to fall in step as they walked back toward the supposed road. The trip was not long at all—just a few small streams to cross and there the road was. The girl stood beside it, looking both ways. One way looked familiar, and she could see some distant landmarks she vaguely recognized. The other way was not familiar at all.

"The longer you walk, the more you will see how far you've come," the cat said matter-of-factly. "You might even remember where the road began—where you began."

"Do you really think so?" the girl asked hesitantly.

The cat grinned as if the question was silly. "Who knows? But the owl told me so." Then the cat turned and headed back toward the forest.

The girl took one step forward, paused, and then asked, "What happens if I leave the road again?"

"Oh, I don't think that will happen," replied the cat over its shoulder.

"Why not?" she called out.

"Because you are now awake."

One Thousand Degrees

The girl thrust her hands into the water; steam rose from the surface. She looked down at them in the cool, dark waters. Although moments before, they were completely consumed by fire, her arms showed no marks. She remembered what it felt like to hold the licking flames in her hands and the struggle of trying to direct the flame around her arm. Her breath grew heavy in her chest, and the strangling grip of her failure tightened around her throat. *Why can't I control this?*

"Again..." her mentor instructed softly from the shadows.

For hours, she attempted to gain control of the wild chaos emanating from within. Her frustration crept from her mouth in gasping words: "Help me." With this prayer, she appealed to the world, in hope that the answer she sought would come quickly. This fire was her burden to bear, and she must work through it for the sake of the ones she loved. These flames were her gift of nature, one she was meant to control.

The girl stood back up determined and lowered her focus into her heart. Her surroundings faded away as she became one with the steady rhythm of her heartbeat. As she focused, she pushed the rhythm faster and faster. The heat in her chest spread into her arms and gathered at the tips of her fingers. With her awareness following the warmth, she envisioned a flame within the darkness of her mind's eye. The pressure at her fingers released, and a small flame danced at each fingertip. From here, her task was clear—to spread the fire up the skin. By shifting the air around her, she could guide her flame up her arms and toward her elbows. Slowly she coaxed the tender flame to consume the oxygen surrounding her arm. As the flame grew, so did her fear.

A sudden sense of dread enveloped her as torment emerged from the depths of her memory. *Please no. Not now. Recall anything but this.* The full force of the image struck her like an unavoidable blow to the stomach. Before her eyes, she saw faces twisted with screams. They ran from her as their world was swallowed by flames. Her voice ran out of her lungs, and the fire enveloping her arms burst forth, abruptly knocking the girl back. The girl dug her feet into the earth to brace herself against the pulse of the explosion. Pushing forward, she drove her arms back into the water.

Only when the steam dissipated did she let out a sigh between her clenched teeth. The remnants of her rage still lingered in her body. It wasn't that long ago that her uncontrollable flames burned her village. Since then, she had spent most of her time here in the watery coves along the far side of the island, too guilty and ashamed to face those she put into jeopardy. She sank to the damp floor.

Once again, her mentor's candid voice emanated from the cave's darkened depth: "Give it your all or give up."

The girl released another sigh. She couldn't give up—that wasn't an option. Not unless she decided to abandon everything she held dear. It was her duty with this gift of fire to offer a warm embrace for her people, but this would not work if she burned the world every time she lost her temper. She just needed control and focus. The girl pressed her hands into the soil and pushed her body aside to make room for her feet to stand. She steadied herself to begin again but hesitated.

"Why do you resist past woes?" asked her mentor inquisitively.

The girl looked up to the dome of her secluded alcove and followed its shape to the water-worn entrance. The ocean beyond shimmered with the light of the full moon. The girl looked longingly at the calm waters as a feeling of weightlessness stirred within her. The urge to fight the calm shook her soul. She wanted to scream out against it and brush it from her. She quivered with the internal debate of these opposing sensations. One part of herself craved the serene calmness of the ocean, while the other wanted to burst forth and displace all that surrounded her.

"What if I go too far?" the girl asked into the space of the cave.

"What if you go so far that you come back around?" her mentor's voice answered back.

The girl looked down at her bare feet, blackened and calloused from bracing herself against the exploding flames. Getting through this ordeal, she mused, was much like the transformation her feet had gone through. The only way she had been able to build up the toughness of her feet was to press into the ground when the force of flames turned upon her with its ferocity. If she didn't press her feet into the ground, she would be knocked off them, and then her feet would remain soft, never toughening. The girl knew that in this same way she must expose her mind to the memory that haunted her. She knew she had to experience it fully, to embrace it before she could become hardened by it and not react. Yet, each time her heart spiked with emotion, with the horror of her mistakes, her flames responded in the same way, such that they exploded from her very hands.

"Explosive to focused," the girl reaffirmed her mantra into the night.

"Letting go doesn't mean giving up," the night echoed back.

"Tsk," breathed the girl, turning her head sharply from the ocean scenery and following the path back to the darkened pool of the cave. Here she stayed until a sliver of sun crept up from beyond the horizon. As it rose higher in the sky, its light illuminated the once-darkened cave. The walls showed their artwork of scorched earth from the times the flames had consumed her. These marks were her lessons, and their presence was her mentor—an inner voice calling her to self-mastery.

Warrior Medicine

"My child, do you know why you are here?" asked the elder, turning toward her, laying out a blanket, and kneeling upon the earth. She motioned for the girl to join her on the blanket.

"I am injured. I am here to purge weakness."

"Is that all?"

"I am not sure what you mean by that." The girl was puzzled by the nature of the question.

The elder explained further, "My child, we all contain weakness, for we are only human. Sometimes that weakness is hidden and tucked away within our souls. We come here to this hollow and ask Saturn to protect us as we journey inward to discover strength."

The girl sat in silence, contemplating the elder's words. The air around her hung still, carrying the smell of moist earth. The only sounds were of their gentle breaths and their echoed voices.

"My child, you are not here because you sustained a bodily wound. You are here because you could not sense the attack fast enough…not because you are unskilled, which you are not, but because you had a blind spot. A blind spot only forms when something within is not honored into consciousness but kept hidden and secret from even yourself. It is time for it to come to the surface before that blind spot brings more dire consequences. Your soul will thank you, and your mind shall be at ease." The elder paused to let her words take root. "Are you ready for Saturn's teaching?"

The girl's resolve held firm within her. "Yes."

"Then we begin. Lie here, my child. First, we must ask Earth to help us see clearly the veil of Saturn—this is the boundary you must overcome to find true strength."

The elder reached for a vial containing a liquid made of water and a shredded native root. "Close your eyes. When I say to open, open them wide." The elder placed one drop in each tear duct. "Now!"

The stinging was one of the worst feelings the girl had ever experienced. She squeezed her eyes shut tightly, not daring to try to open them again. At first, she thought, *This is it; I am going to be blind for the rest of my life.* Then she remembered no one had become blind from this ordeal in the past and put her faith in her elder. As she brought her attention to her breath, she wondered, *Why am I here?*

Her own voice spoke back into her mind: *To purge the emotions holding you back from stepping into your power.*

The girl was strong, but sometimes there was a fear of her own strength. She tended to hold back during training, fearful she would hurt someone. She felt the conviction to prove herself to her tribe and to become a strong warrior to protect her people. Yet, she couldn't help but feel as though she could give more.

The stinging in her eyes slowly began to subside, but still she held them closed, breathing deep into her body. She could feel the tension around her injury begin to loosen. The event became clear within her mind as did the sensations of her body—a stiffening of her muscles where there should have been a release, a shortness of breath that should have been full and deep. Uncertainty had flashed through her with doubts of where to focus. That moment of hesitation unfolded in slow motion within her mind—hesitation on so many levels...

hesitation of will, hesitation of faith, hesitation of mind and body. And in that same instant, she watched her opponent's spear thrust toward her.

As the stinging now fully dissipated, the girl slowly opened her eyes. The world around her was dim yet sharp. The elder's figure was as clear as the moon against a cloudless midnight sky. She sat up slowly in deep thought. The elder eyed her carefully yet said nothing.

The girl acknowledged that she would need to be the first one to speak. "I am ready to sit with Saturn," she said quietly. Thoughts still buzzed within her mind—thoughts of why she was here, what she was here to learn, and what was holding her back.

"Turn around, my child, and drink the water before you." The elder motioned as she spoke.

The girl turned her injured back toward the elder and faced a giant bowl of water. "All of it?" the girl asked, raising an eyebrow.

"Yes, my child."

Although the girl could not see it, she swore she could feel the elder smile. The girl took a deep breath, readied herself, and drank from the bowl until her belly was beyond full. The girl felt bloated and ready to burst.

"We will now burn the gateways that allow Saturn to enter the body, mind, and soul. One gateway for each." The elder took an incense stick, burned short from the numerous ceremonies past, and lit it with a small candle. Three small marks were made in the skin just below the area of the girl's wound. The sensation surprised the girl but hurt much less than the injury itself.

"This contains the essence of Saturn, which will be placed on the gateways."

The elder held a wooden stick with a ceraceous coating. She scraped the surface of the stick with a damp blade, forming three small pellets. "What happens next is up to you. Remember, this is the time to purge the illness from the body so you may hear Saturn strong within you."

"I am ready," the girl confirmed with a long exhale.

The elder pressed the waxy pellets on each of the burned gateways. The girl could feel a slight burning sensation, and as the elder began to drum lightly, the girl's heartbeat grew louder and stronger. The girl's body tingled all over, and her internal temperature rose quickly. Her ears rang and pulsed. Her heart seemed to ascend through her body to her head.

She heard a voice other than her own within her mind. "Feel your heartbeat; that's what drives you. Follow it!"

The girl breathed out heavily. She looked down at her hands. The blood in her veins had turned black, and her skin's tan had almost completely faded to white. *I've been poisoned!* The girl's thoughts raced with panic, her mind frantically searching for a remedy to the sudden flood of unfamiliar sensations in her body.

Nausea suddenly hit the girl. She crawled off her blanket to the edge of the wall and purged the contents of her stomach upon the earthen floor. The elder's drum beat louder in celebration of the purge. Waves of nausea flooded over the girl. She purged several more times until fatigue began to take hold of her.

She heard the words "I can't" slip through her lips quietly. Yet in the cave, the words seemed to echo off the walls only to be thrown back at her along with the sound of the drum.

The same voice returned within her mind: "False."

Another wave of nausea, another purge. Soon the words "I can't" echoed within her purges. She began to see the symbolism of this—she was releasing the words "I can't" from her being. Their hold upon her weakened. Images flooded her mind, memories and feelings from many times in her life, shedding themselves from her with every purge. A newfound strength took the place of her fatigue. And at last, she felt empty. The drumming stopped, and the images slowly faded.

Suddenly her vision went dark, and she felt a hand on the side of her head. The elder gently slid her away from the cave's wall and rested her once again upon the blanket in the center of the room. Her head was set upon something soft, and a hand ran through her hair.

"Rest, my child," the elder's soft voice comforted the girl. "You did well, young warrior."

The girl breathed softly. She replayed the once racing memories now more slowly in her mind. She ran through their meanings and pondered how they were all connected. She recognized that the common fear that held her in hesitation was the fear of going too far—going too far to a place from which she could never come back to her present reality. It was the fear of letting go of everything she knew to be true about her life, but this fear no longer dwelled inside. A new strength rested itself within her. She felt ready to dive into the abyss of the unknown and fully step into her power.

In her head, a boisterous voice resounded: "Now it's time for the real work to begin!"

With the Power Inside, She Flies

Her heart beat like a drum throughout her body as she moved effortlessly through the air. Her soul vibrated; every inch of her was activated. Her wings pulsed solidly and firmly as she soared higher above the quickly diminishing landscape. With each long, powerful stroke, she gained height upon the ground below her.

The girl's lungs burned as she approached her body's limit. *Two more strokes,* she thought. *I can go up two more.* The sun felt so close. Its blaze pierced her skin like needles. She gathered its warmth with her wings and wrapped them tightly around her. For a moment, she hung there, in suspended weightlessness, before gravity tugged her back into a free fall.

The drum of her heart quickly increased in tempo as air sped upward around her. She closed her eyes, counting the beats and listening carefully. Here in the free fall, freedom enveloped her; a stillness overcame her. She felt timeless. Her whole body tingled, senses wide open. She observed every shift in pressure and felt her velocity increase. Though her eyes were closed, she could "see" the world around her—the ground rising up to greet her. The potential of energy built gradually in her shoulder blades, itching to be released.

Flying toward the Sun was one way to push boundaries. Another, far more revealing in strength, was falling back to the earth below. This was a test for warriors, forbidden to children wishing to prove their mettle. Too many failed to open their eyes and wings in time.

The image of the ground ripping away their gift of flight and their life flashed in the girl's mind.

She subdued the fear stirring and held at bay the doubt insisting on her attention. *What if I miscalculate? What if I am wrong?* She pushed these thoughts behind her. They would do her no good, only pull her focus away from the demands of staying centered. She had trained for this day, prepared herself for this moment. Resolution steeled her nerves; a familiar calm washed over her, which she experienced as extended and pronounced silence between each heartbeat.

Almost there. The girl remembered her spotter, ready and waiting to give warning or intervene if she did not react in time. With mutual trust, this bond fused together their sense of the other, woven into one unified awareness—a connection that was threaded through all the warriors of her tribe.

The girl's instinctual desires suddenly flared up like a great internal fire, as piercing as the Sun. This was it; the drumming in her heart built into a crescendo. *Now!* The message came through as clear as day. A choir of voices all singing together in her mind—the voices of her inner self, the voice of her spotter, and the voices of her tribe witnessing her initiation.

She opened her eyes and wings simultaneously, catching the wind beneath them, forcing her body upright. Sonic waves of energy from her heart flooded out into every part of her. Just in time, her feet struck the ground with such a force that the earth rippled out in all directions. The drumbeat hit its final note, the vibration of energy released and reverberated around her.

The girl breathed heavily, eyes set in determination toward the horizon, gratitude swelling through her heart. Today was the day she became a warrior for her people.

God Is in the Word

The girl's chant filled the space around her. The walls echoed the chorus back to her. Every cell of her body hummed with its vibration. Again and again, she repeated the sacred words—sacred by nothing other than the intrinsic meaning of the seed syllables uttered with her very lips.

The girl paused…listening to the reverb alive in each cell. *I think…* she began the chant again. Using the words like a sword to cut away the muck of thought itself, she repeated them once more. At first loudly, out into the space, but gently over time, they grew soft until they bubbled up only in the deep recess of her inner mind; yet still their frequency was woven into the very fabric of her existence—both within her and as the space around her. Body and space, space and body interwoven with the thread of her words.

Again she paused, and silence encompassed her like a warm blanket. At the edge of her mind, she felt a thought encroach upon this silent territory. *I am…* Again she chanted. The deep vowels in her throat, created by the movement of her tongue and mouth, offered her a point of focus. She dove deep in its direction without hesitation or misgivings. She knew this flow so well. Every morning and every evening, she called to these words to bring her home.

What was her home? The silence that revealed itself every time she paused. In those pauses, she relished in its unfolding. Silence, the undertone beneath all sound. She saw in her mind's eye, where the sound bloomed from, like a lotus poking up from dark mud. The sound shone in its glory like a jewel, reflecting a pure white light into many different colors. Compassion filled her, washing through every muscle and bone. Gratitude warmed her heart, reaching out into every fingertip, toe, and hair follicle.

These words, these sounds of ancient wisdom—they all pointed to the same place; they all led her back to the space of silence, the place of all potential. The potential manifested itself through these words into form, created by the vibration of sound—only to dissolve back again into the stillness of silence. Like a wave caressing the shore, she swayed in the dance of sound and silence.

She paused again, along with a sigh of relief. The image slowly faded into the black background, its imprint melting back into the void where it had originated from. This was her, her true self—this presence, this knowing, this being. This silence was her essence; everything that lay on top of it was like the sound that came from her—beautiful yet fleeting. The only consistent thing that remained was silence.

Tears streamed down her face. What they held within them was everything and nothing, every thing and no thing. She breathed and oxygen filled her lungs, flooding her body with vitality. And she remembered: *I am the sound born from silence.* And she chanted.

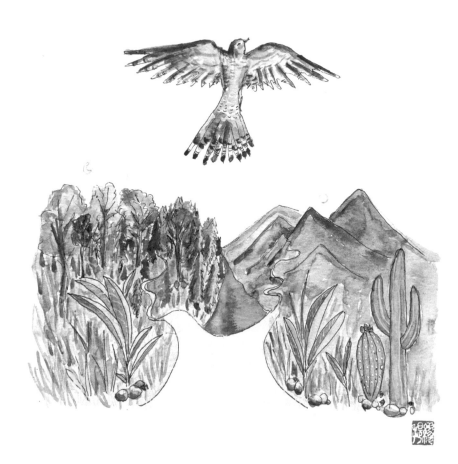

Two Roads Diverged

The poem echoed in the girl's head: "Two roads diverged in a wood, and I—I took the one less traveled by, And that has made all the difference."[2] She stood now at a fork in the road, and yet they both looked equally untraveled. Her mind buzzed with thoughts surmising the consequences of each path. Both were unknown, and both were unmarked on the map held in her hands.

The hills she had been walking recently were quite nice—greenish-yellow rolling hills lining a fairly easygoing path until she reached this fork. Looking down one path, she saw the incline turn sharply upward and become quite rocky. She would have to climb with much strength up the rock wall to cross the mountain pass that lay in the distance.

Turning her gaze down the other path, she thought it seemed quite mellow at first. But as the girl stared down that way, she saw quite clearly a dense forest waiting for her just past the curve. Its dark and eerie aura told her intuition that the forest would be thick with underbrush and many trees closely knit together. It would take much finesse to maneuver her way through. Each road only let her view her future trail up until a certain point and then she would face a wall—one of rock or one of trees. Down both, the girl could foresee her doom: one held a fall to her death; the other would have her lost forever in the dark.

---

2 Frost, Robert. "The Road Not Taken." 1915. *Poetry Foundation*, Poetry Foundation, www.poetryfoundation.org/poems/44272/the-road-not-taken. Accessed Dec. 2023.

The girl felt this decision weigh heavily on her shoulders. The pressure of choice burdened her every thought. She would have to sit with this for a moment, as it was not an easy choice. She sighed and slumped to the ground. The whirling of her mind did not stop, spinning on and on. She held each option in her body in hopes to discern in which direction to go. *If only I had a sign*, the girl thought, feeling dismayed. The irony of the signpost standing erect in front of her seemed to taunt her with glee. Its worn and weathered wood told her the last time these roads were cared for by human hands was well in the past. The names of the directions, as far as she could tell beyond their faded script, were obvious and vague. They could have both been labeled "somewhere" for all the help they gave.

Spinning 'round and 'round, the thoughts and visions in her head raged on. She contemplated each journey and weighed the pros and cons. One side of the scale held the challenges she would have to overcome, and on the other, she could foresee the rewards of these lessons. The girl imagined the view she would see at the peak of the mountain—the vast perception and height of the land's greatest majesty. Tilting her head toward the forest, she mused upon what would await her there—finding a sense of direction even in the dark was the lesson that path would bestow upon her. *Oh, what should I choose?* she pondered with frustration.

The thoughts in her head had become a full-blown whirlwind with her as the eye of the storm. Her body began to ache, encouraging her to move forward with a choice. But the back-and-forth movement of her mind was making her dizzy and barely able to see clearly. Just for a moment she wished they would stand still, for time to stop and alleviate this pressure.

As her thoughts flashed 'round and 'round, she caught a glimpse of a memory long forgotten, a time in her youth when she made choices without a clear vision of the future or an anchor in the past, a time when she lived in the present. But she was a child back then—would time still stop for her now? She would have to attempt this feat once more or be doomed to spin around endlessly here with no decision made, confronting this fork in the road for all eternity.

She steadied herself upon the ground and began to breathe deep and full. As she focused on her breath, her senses came in more clearly. The touch of cool air on her skin, the smell of dewy grass among the gentle breeze. The warmth of the sun caressed her exposed skin, and there was a slightly sweet taste upon her tongue. As these sensations grew in her awareness, her vision began to clear. The thoughts on the merry-go-round were slowing down; without their momentum spinning around, the storm gently dissolved.

Her vision then expanded past the sight of her eyes, as if she flew above the land itself. Looking down in her mind's eye, she saw herself sitting there patiently as the winds of thought stilled around her. The gravity of her choice no longer bound her to that cumbersome fork in the road. She could see now how inconsequential this matter was in the speck of the present moment. For beyond the tall mountain cliffs lay part of the dense forest, and beyond the dense forest lay another rocky pass. The lessons that awaited her would come no matter which path she chose; the trials and tribulations that this journey demanded of her would come with time.

She continued to watch the story of these paths unfold in her mind's eye, letting the land speak to her. Still ahead, she felt the land guiding her forward in its tale; she followed the interweaving lessons, the climaxes and sudden twists of this plot of land, until she came to the last chapter. There she saw with lucid awareness a path of destiny, a path that came from the two roads merging once again beyond these contests of will.

With this reverie, she recognized a deeper understanding. Two paths still lay before her, awaiting her precious choice; yet the decision was not of which land she wished to transverse first—it was a matter of choosing with patient presence and in doing so, revealing a heartfelt direction. One that moved toward faith versus the tempest of careful analysis with a mind blinded by the fear of choice. Again the poem resounded with her inner voice: "Two roads diverged in a wood, and I—I took the one less traveled by, And that has made all the difference."

Where the two roads led mattered not, for the lessons of her journey would come when they came. The roads diverging before her, which held her attention now, were paths of faith or fear. *I took the one less traveled,* she thought with a deep, full breath. Remembering the stillness of presence, she turned and walked forward with a resolute stride. *And that has made all the difference.*

Surrender

That was the last straw! The girl burst out of her front door and ran straight into the roaring rain, head held high. She paused to take in her surroundings. The water rushed to meet her skin, weighing down the fabric clinging to her. The pull of it urged her to kneel. "Kneel down to the power of the heavens," it commanded her. But she would not yield—she could not. Too long was she held hostage within her own home, pacing her confines amid the storm, resisting its drive toward madness.

She lifted her chin to the dark space above her, contemplating ways to bring an end to the storm's reign over her world. How do you take up arms against an act of God, when your reach is far too short to strike your enemy? A streak of lightning ran across the sky, ordering her to bite her tongue. Its thunder shook the earth as if to say, "Try me." No longer could she remain quiet. She had held her breath for ages, waiting for the storm to cease. Finally, she would be louder than thunder.

She clenched her eyes shut against the biting drops assaulting her. Feeling frustration and anger press against her lips, she placed her struggle within a single breath and released it with a scream. Her voice bellowed up, into the darkened sky. She did not relent until the last molecule of air had left her lungs. Succeeding her only hopes of victory against an unseen foe, the voice of God roared back. The girl flinched but stood her ground. *It wasn't enough. Again!* She screamed once more. Another encore from the heavens resounded down upon her. *Again!* Each time the girl flung her voice at the sky, it drowned before it ever reached the clouds.

The girl stood quiet, attempting to gather her breath for another attack. Her ears rang with the echo of the voice released. "What do you want from me?" she yelled at the sky. The wind cut through her clothing in response; it took away her breath. The girl dropped to her knees, and her palms met the ground. Her fingers dug into the sodden earth. She gasped for air but choked on moisture—all the girl needed was her breath. She prayed silently, "I want to live. Give me back my breath, and I shall surrender."

As she focused on her breath, the noise of the storm disappeared into the background of her darkened world. When one breath ended, the girl took another. And another. *What is this feeling?* she thought. It was not a silence of sound but a silence of being. A smile emerged upon her mouth, gentle and with ease. The darkness behind her closed eyelids began to lighten—not the quick flash of lightning in the sky but as a soft glow instead.

As the girl opened her eyes, her vision awakened to warm rays of sunlight peeking through developing cracks in the unified gray above. The girl felt a raindrop fall onto each cheek, but this water was not from the sky—this water was from within—and like the rain rushing toward the earth, the girl released her body to gravity. She lay upon her back, letting the flooded earth cradle her. The built-up tension began to melt away. The only thing left to do was float...and breathe.

The Weight of Our Stories

The girl breathed heavily. The straps of her sack dug deeper into the crest of her shoulders with every step. The same scene continued endlessly in front of her: flatlands with tiny patches of grass here and there and great peaks of mountains in the distance. No matter how far she traveled, it was as though she made no progress.

The sun neared the horizon, warning her to prepare for the evening's chill. A lone tree stood to the side of the road as a suitable resting place. The girl shook off her sack and stretched her back as an attempt to realign her spine.

She slumped against the trunk—the bark was gnarled and twisted as if being wrung out by unseen sources. She reached for her lantern and the heavy sack she had been carrying. Opening the bag revealed its contents—a huge pile of books. These were no ordinary books though; these were her stories—the memories of her life experiences and beliefs she knew to be true. Every night, she read through every book and recorded her day into new blank pages until she eventually nodded off to sleep. In the morning, she rose to repack her life and continue on her journey with them once again upon her shoulders—a routine for as long as she could remember. Although fatigue gripped her heart day after day, the vision of her goal in the distance kept her pushing forward.

The following day unfolded more or less the same. Looking again for a tree to rest beneath, she noticed one in the distance, yet this one was already accompanied by the presence of another—a girl, it seemed, a little older than she. The stranger-girl lay on her back chewing a single piece of grass, staring up into the sky.

The girl nodded to this occupant as she passed along to find other refuge for the evening when she heard a voice yell out. "Hey! Hey, you!" the stranger shouted. "Where ya goin'? Ya know there ain't another tree for a long while. You should rest here while ya can."

The girl hesitated for a moment and saw the assessment to be true—there was not another tree in sight for a long while. As she approached, she asked the stranger, "Are you sure there is room for me and my load?" She heaved the sack to the ground, creating a puff of dust that hung in the air.

Still lying on her back, the girl gave her a toothy grin, switching the blade of grass in her mouth. "Well, sure there is. I don't have that burden anymore."

The girl looked around, and sure enough, there was not another sack in sight. The girl sat down next to this stranger, welcoming the rest and weight off her body. As the sun dipped below the horizon, as per her normal, she prepared her lantern, her pen, and opened her sack.

The stranger-girl simply watched for a bit but then let out a long whistle as she unpacked the first few books. "Wooo-wee, that's quite a haul ya got there. Probably gonna take ya all night, huh?"

The girl simply continued her process and then paused for a moment and asked, "What happened to all your stories?"

The stranger-girl jumped up to her feet, did a quick twirl around, and then bowed. Upon lifting just her head, she exclaimed with a full grin: "I burned them!" She stood erect, laughing with her whole body, and then she held up her hands wide open to the sky and yelled into the night, "I burned them all!" She did a jig circling around the tree, clicking her heels together in delight.

The girl was astonished, taken aback by the very possibility. She burned them? You could do that? And so she inquired, "Why would you burn your stories?"

This energetic stranger spun on her heel to face her. "Well, long story short, they were too dang heavy, I tell ya. Felt like I was never gonna reach them mountains." She thrust her thumb over her shoulder toward the peaked range in the distance. "Ain't ya tired and sore carrying all that weight day in and out?"

The girl did feel quite sore. The more she felt into her body, the more apparent the aches and pains became. Her eyelids felt as heavy as the sack she carried, and she craved nothing more than to surrender herself to the ground and to never get up again. She couldn't stop here though; she had to reach her destination. The top of those mountains waited patiently for her arrival. She glanced down at her pile of books. All these stories she had carried for so long—it seemed unimaginable to burn them.

The stranger-girl followed her gaze and reached out for one of the books.

"Hey, give that back! That story is not for you." The girl tried to snatch it back, but this stranger was just too quick and her body was sluggish.

The stranger-girl quickly scrambled up the tree to a low-hanging branch, opened her book, and began flipping through the pages. The girl simply didn't have enough energy to follow her. The stranger's voice then came from the branch overhead. "This story ain't for you either. Seems a bit outdated to where ya are now, if ya ask me."

"What do you mean 'outdated'?" the girl asked with frustration lining her tone.

The stranger-girl swung upside down hanging by her knees and pointed to a passage on the page: "Ya see right here? This story was from a different time; you were in a different place." She turned the book back toward her. "The ocean, I think, maybe a sea? Hard to tell which. But do ya see an ocean 'round here?" Before the girl could reply, the stranger-girl went on, "Nope. No ocean. No sea. This story ain't relevant anymore, so why do ya hold on to it?"

The girl once more tried to snatch the book away, but the stranger withdrew the book from her reach just as her fingers grazed the cover. She spoke sternly to this stranger and now thief. "That story reminds me of where I have been, what I have seen, and what I've experienced. It made me who I am today."

The stranger-girl's reply came now from higher in the tree. "Well, sure it did, but that doesn't mean ya gotta carry it with ya currently. Never gonna reach those mountains if ya don't let some of this go."

The girl snorted in response and countered with irritation, "Then why don't you help me carry them?"

Laughter echoed down. "Ain't my stories. But I'll tell ya this: I can help ya with something else."

"And what would that be?" the girl said glumly. Then suddenly she felt a presence land behind her, causing her to jump with surprise.

She spun around to find the stranger-girl grinning with a full-tooth smile and gleaming, with fire in her eyes. "I'll help ya burn them."

The girl turned away and stood in careful contemplation. When she thought of the burden of carrying her stories another day, despair swept through her. The girl imagined burning the book this stranger-girl still held in her hands, perusing its pages. It was a story about when she had been thrown into the ocean as a joke. The strong current pulled her under, and she almost drowned. She vowed she would never let someone do that to her again—it was an important lesson, and she kept that story to remind herself that she couldn't trust others with her life.

The girl suddenly felt weary and needed to sit down before she could speak. "These are my stories. How will I remember them?"

The stranger-girl smiled gently and came to sit by her side. "How 'bout ya tell them to me?"

The girl was shocked. "Do you have the time to listen?"

The stranger-girl giggled and shrugged. "I got nowhere to be, and I'm here now."

For the next few days, they swapped stories beneath the tree—turns out they had more than a few stories in common. Sure, the circumstances were different, but they shared common themes.

One night, this not-so-much-of-a-stranger-anymore asked the girl, "Why are ya goin' to the mountains?"

The girl sighed—stories that had led her to that decision stirred in her mind. Finding the best words to describe her reasoning, she said, "I want to prove that I am capable of something more than ordinary."

The other-girl smiled with compassion. "Ahh, I see. And, um, who you tryin' to prove yourself to, exactly?"

The girl looked down at the lantern illuminating their quaint camp. "Everyone," she replied.

The other-girl snickered. "I ain't mean no disrespect, but that's a lot of people."

The girl laughed with her. "I guess you're right. That is a lot of people...Perhaps I am trying to prove myself worthy of something. Recognition. It often feels that I am not seen for who I really am."

The other-girl gave her a big, toothy grin. "Well, that's cause you're hidden 'neath all these dang stories," she replied as she nudged her chin toward the pile of books strewn about the ground. "No wonder no one is seein' ya—they don't know where the real you is under all this," she said, again motioning toward the piles.

The other-girl popped up from her seated position and rummaged through one of the stacks. "Looky here—see this story?" The other-girl shook the book in front of her. "This story where ya think you ain't good enough? This ain't gonna get you up that mountain. Only good as a weight on ya shoulders."

The girl rubbed her still sore shoulders, lost in thought, until the sound of shuffling brought her attention to her companion, the other-girl, gathering a pile of sticks with dead leaves and dry grass. Without a word, she grabbed the lantern and smashed it onto the pile, instantly igniting the whole thing.

The fire quickly blazed into a full roar. The girl gazed into its flames, the warmth penetrating her aching bones until a soft thud landed by her feet. There upon the ground was her story of "not good enough." She looked up at her companion, standing with a direct gaze into her eyes, and a smile spread across her face. "It's time to let that go—never gonna go anywhere with that holdin' ya back."

The girl gingerly picked up the book, treating it like a broken bird fallen from its nest. Turning it over in her hands, she recalled this story of misspoken and hurtful words that happened so long ago. What cost did she pay to carry this with her day after day? It was time to let it go and free herself from its burden. With that thought, the girl tossed the book into the flames, and her companion howled in delight, dancing a victory jig around the fire.

She embraced the girl in a full bear hug and then looked her straight in the eyes and gleefully exclaimed, "OK! Time for the next one!"

And so it went on...book after book into the fire, each celebrated with a jig as the story dissolved. The final pages now burned, and the girl's newfound friend came to her with a blank journal and said, "This story is yours to write. Ain't no one's place to tell ya who ya are. Rewrite it as many times as ya like, and burn the ones that only act as weights."

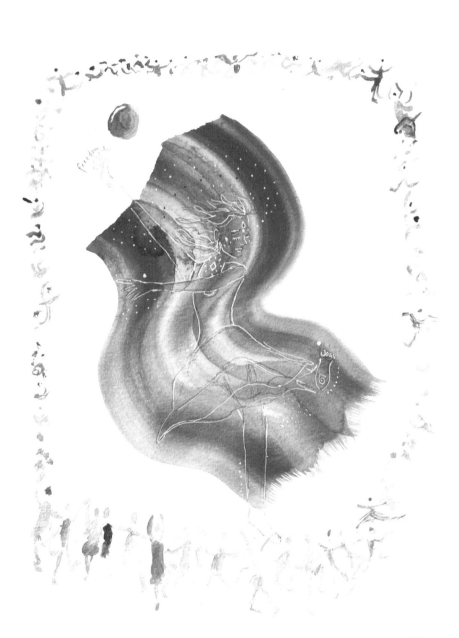

When She Danced

*I*s *it over? Is this the end of my torment?* A strange sensation washed through the girl as she stared out into the ecstatic crowd. A sensation of intensity, closely related to thrill, tickled the girl's inner body, and the hair on her arms stood up with chills. *Is the past really behind me?*

The beat of the song drummed through the earthen floor. Its deep and steady rhythm pulled her slowly from the confines of her mind, where she was held captive for so long. The vibrational hum stimulated the nerves of her feet, sending a surge of energy up through her legs and into her spine.

She stood at the edge of an unseen precipice, with the desire to release the chains that bound her to her place. No longer could her fear and doubt keep her contained. In this moment, she would choose the eternal freedom that came with this leap of faith.

She grasped at her chest out of fear that her heart would jump out of her body. She burst forth from the edge of the gathering, her skirt flying out behind her as the sound of the music pulled her into the dance. The draped cloth along her arms caught the wind, encouraging this moment of flight. The air rushed through her hair as she spun and jumped to the rhythm coursing through her veins. The girl's awareness dropped down into her body, her skin pulsing with the music's vibration.

The world, for once, began to make sense. The girl danced without hesitation as she guided her elation into the fluid twists and turns of her body. Tears streamed down her cheeks and rested upon her lips, curled upward in an effortless smile. She didn't know whether to laugh or to cry, so she did both. There was no pain, no doubt, no shame, no guilt—every cell in her being sang through her motion. She didn't care that the muscles in her feet ached—the ache was a reminder of the life still within her.

With eyes closed, she melted into a trance, becoming one with the flow. She was present yet elsewhere at the same time—present in her reality, yet distant from the world she once knew. Sliding into her pocket of rhythm, her body became one with the melodies. Her intuition whispered each note before they sang, and she followed its lead, never early and never late, always within the river of notes—even her tears glittered rhythmically.

Her lungs expanded quickly, trying to keep up with her movement. They stretched her will with the urge to keep going. She couldn't stop—she wouldn't until the last note was sung. She could feel the building of energy in her body, which she redirected to places that creaked and groaned within her. The muscles she once maintained with vigor had become feeble in her captivity.

But no more—this was her dance of freedom, and she would not rest until every cell in her body was reactivated with the rhythm palpitating in her chest. She pushed the flow of energy into every joint, every ligament, willing it to become alive once more. She allowed her body to be played by the sound and uncovered a frequency she had long sought: the fluidity of water, the quintessence of life itself; the essential necessity of its nature was rising up within her.

If she could, she would drown in it, drown herself in this language of sound and let it consume her. She felt a bond between her body and the harmony, a bond beyond space and time. This feeling so new yet one of remembrance—the feeling of bliss and liberation from within. It was then she felt the touch of the holy mother and her divine hand of release. The warm, gentle tenderness swept through the girl's being and revealed a great purpose. Everything, including herself, had meaning.

The people around her, who had disappeared from her awareness, slowly dropped back into her vision. They were no longer single entities dancing within their own capacity but had become a single mass of aspects twirling around together, united in the beat of their hearts and the stomping of their feet—and she herself stood right in the middle of it. In her trance, she had gravitated toward the very center. And so she too twirled in the unfolding fractal; she spun as all of life danced around her, letting the wave of existence carry her around and around.

Soon the motion became effortless, as if she were truly flying on the fabric of wings. This cosmic spiral of motion grounded itself into the earth and pulsed into a starry sky above them. This freedom was theirs, and after this night, it would not be so easily forgotten.

Comfort in the Silence

"Soo...what's your favorite color?" The girl smiled in anticipation, eyes shining bright.

"Hmmm." The boy looked up for only a moment. "Blue," he proclaimed.

"Blue? Why blue? Everyone likes blue."

"I think blue is nice."

"Really? That's really why you like it? Because it's nice?" she questioned, probing further.

"Yeah," he said with a shrug.

The girl swung her feet idly below her. The fence she was sitting on still felt damp from the morning's rain.

"It's also the color of the sky," the boy continued.

The girl looked up at the now clear sky, feeling the warmth of the day settle into the atmosphere. The air was crisp and fresh, so she took a deep breath.

"I really wish I could fly, you know? Wouldn't that be fun?" he playfully inquired.

The girl stretched her arms out wide. "I have a lot of flying dreams—does that count?"

"Yeah, of course. Just because you are asleep doesn't make it any less real."

"True. A little trickier to navigate, though." She paused thoughtfully. "Where would you go? If you could fly?"

The boy looked puzzled as many answers flooded his head. His eyebrows knitted together as he tried to decide.

"And it could be anywhere in the universe," she emphasized, nudging him with her shoulder.

"Pluto!" The boy grinned.

"*Pluto?*" she exclaimed. "It's so cold there!"

"But it gets such a bad rap. First it's a planet and then all of sudden...nope! No more planethood. Poor guy."

"*Ha ha!*" the girl's laugh filled the air.

"OK then, where would you go?"

The girl scanned the world around her. Gentle rolling hills created a serpent-like horizon that continued past what she could see. The grass in the fields was lush and a vibrant green. The distant trees lining the nearby dirt road swayed with a gentle breeze.

He looked out to the landscape with her. "If only there was all the time in the world, huh?" the boy mused out loud.

The girl smiled, turning her head to watch the boy gaze out into the distance.

"Would you live forever if you could?" he asked, changing the subject.

"I honestly think I would get bored," she replied.

The boy leaned forward, holding himself at an angle to the top of the fence, ready to leap from his seat at any moment. "Bored? How could you get bored watching life happen?"

"Because life is just a cycle," she stated matter-of-factly.

"It seems a bit boring when you put it that way."

The girl paused and then corrected: "OK, well, maybe it's more of a spiral."

He waited patiently for her to elaborate, settling back into a leisurely posture.

She explained further, "It's the same circular pattern, but each time you come back to something, it gets a bit deeper."

The boy's eyebrows knitted together again as he pondered her words.

With nothing more to say about it, the girl simply sat in a contented manner.

"So...what's your favorite color?" the boy asked, breaking the long, comfortable silence.

The Sea of Dreams

The girl's toes hit the water, sending a shock wave of chill up her spine, snapping her from her trance. Her eyes widened at the stark change; aversion penetrated her mind, sending her whirling in the other direction. Moving slowly into the water would not be an option—she would have to dive in, she concluded. A shiver ran down her spine as she stripped her body bare.

"A leap of faith," she announced out loud as a proclamation of her resolution.

Her body shook though there was no wind to chill her. She could already feel the weight of the water pulling her under. The sea expanding wide beckoned her to its shore. She could feel it pulling at her chest like a lover just past her reach. She could not resist the draw and heaviness before her. She stood there just beyond the water's reach and imagined herself diving in, yet her body exhibited no response to move any closer. To leave everything behind, all that she knew and loved, in exchange for all that she desired—this tore her will in two. She could still turn around and make the journey back to that which was familiar; yet missing from this familiarity was the sense of home. Her soul was still searching—searching for something to call her own.

Her eyes sought out the other side of the sea, wanting to know what lay ahead after crossing. She stared hard into the distance, trying to force an image of recognition. Perhaps the image would not come because she did not know what she really wanted. The girl gave a sigh of exasperation, more expressive than what was needed.

This is silly, she thought. *What exactly is holding me back?* She felt the tether in her body, keeping her feet firmly planted. Like a hook in the back of her heart, she felt resistance holding her where she stood.

Degraded by this struggle, she hung her head and stared deep into the water. A blurry version of herself mirrored her lowly spirit. Though for a moment, as the waves of the tide rippled through her expression, she thought she saw it smile and laugh instead of being frozen with indecision. As quickly as it flashed, it disappeared. Once more she was looking at her own reflection, searching for something that was no longer there.

As she peered across the sea, a great disturbance moved the surface of the water; yet no wind or anything seen had caused such a tide. There was something in the water—perhaps a mighty beast. Her mind raced with flashes of ideas, of what awaited her in the depths of the sea. She backed away another step, wanting to return to that which she had known; yet she knew if she yielded to the fear, only defeat would greet her at the door.

Back and forth she debated until worn with fatigue. She stared off into the distance, to the fabled shore, trying to get a glimpse of something—anything—that would await her there. Her mind raced with doubt and worry that she would not like what she would find; yet the anticipation of discovery left her antsy. With eyes set and determined on her crossing, she gazed once more into the void of mystery—and that was when the horizon shifted, like her reflection just before. A mirage shimmered into existence as an outline of a door.

She remembered this door appearing when "She of a Thousand Names" came to her, in her waking dream. During the last full moon, just as the last light of day was counting its final sheep, the voice of She called to her as a chosen one destined to cross the sea. A true honor bestowed upon her, the girl hardly believed it at first.

When she asked the elder what the door could mean, the old woman responded with a chuckle and asked her, "What do you think?"

The girl sat down in her chair, shoulders shrugged forward, and answered mostly to herself, "Anything."

The wise eyes of the elder crinkled with her smile. She leaned in close and whispered, "Exactly." The wise woman stood erect, waited but a moment, and then continued, "A door is a passage that She is offering to you. It is your choice on whether or not you wish to walk through. Are you determined to leave this life behind? I would think so or She would not be calling to you."

The girl looked down at the floor, deep in thought, and then asked the elder, "Does anyone ever come back?"

The woman paused with careful thought and then responded with calculated words: "That all depends, my dear. Sometimes we have to let go of ideas of what may be or may not be in this reality to simply let our dreams guide us to the door of possibility. Whether you choose to come back is entirely up to you." The elder gave another cackle, though the source of humor was unknown to the girl, leaving her more confused.

The girl stood still in this memory until the sea pulled her back into the present. She envisioned herself once more taking the plunge, to face the shadows that weighed upon her so heavily. She understood then that what she gravely feared was that walking through that door would mean her death. She didn't want to die, yet at the same time, she didn't want to go back to her old life. The girl had been chosen to make this venture. *She* had called to her, and she was no coward.

Invigorated by this resolve, the girl stood tall with pride. She proudly waded in until the water lapped at her thighs. She eyed the landscape carefully and saw the precipice of land nearby with only water beyond this cliff—so clear and pure it seemed, yet ominous at the same time. The line between her anxiety and thrill was minuscule at best. In her heart, she felt free—no more stabbing pain holding her in place.

The girl raised her hands above her head, took a deep breath, and gracefully dived in. The water closed around her like a sleeve. The chill glided down her body, causing her to shiver. For a moment, her body was no longer human with two arms and feet—she had morphed into a sea creature, long and of one fluid piece.

A flash of panic sparked as the weight of the water pulled her further in; yet her resolution kept her strong, determined to meet this void with courage. She undulated her body, moving herself into deeper water. Deeper and deeper, she swam under, holding her breath until her lungs began to scream for air. But when she searched for the surface, she found that it was no longer there.

She could not feel which way was up or down. Were her eyes open or closed? Which way should she swim to find relief? It was during these thoughts that a door then appeared within her darkened vision— the same door that had revealed itself across the sea and previously in her waking dream. As her only hope of escape, she desperately swam toward it. Reaching for the doorknob, she heard the voice of She.

She spoke to the girl within her head: "Through this door, you get to choose who you want to be: a creature of the land, sky, or sea. This door is an emblem for the power of choice. Realities overlap here on the brink of death; death is but a transition from this to that. Hold the vision of your truth, buried deep within your heart, then open the door to the life you wish to lead."

The girl paused for just a moment when the vision of her heart's desire came clearly. She tightened her grip upon the handle, twisted, and pushed.

This, Too, Belongs

Dear Reader,

It is upon the following pages that I extend a warm invitation for you to weave your own story and spirit. Envision these sheets as a sacred canvas, where you can offer your thoughts, emotions, and experiences much like sacred offerings at an altar at which you seek forgiveness, grace, reconciliation, or remembrance. Whether your tale finds its voice through the eloquence of words or emerges as a vivid illustration, I wholeheartedly welcome you to share a fragment of your inner world. I invite you to express a piece of yourself here because, dear reader, you are never alone on your journey. I am here with you, walking alongside you every step of the way.

_____

_____

_____

_____

_____

_____

_____

_____

_____

_____

_____

_____

Thank you for your story. This, too, belongs.

Feed Your Demons

The creature in front of the girl was hideous, something the likes of an eel. Its body was as black as night with tendrils of foggy smoke trailing about it; its beady eyes bore holes into her soul, and a shiver ran down her spine. The eel-like creature was slick with moisture and cold to the touch.

The girl followed the length of its body back but could not find its tail, for it had wound itself so tightly around her. It was hard to tell where she ended and this creature began. The girl tried to sense its presence, yet everywhere the creature touched felt...numb.

Still, she traced its knotted body, intertwined with her own. She followed it back even further through time and space until she discovered it had also intermeshed itself with her mother. She saw how it clung tightly to her mother's body yet still continued on, continued back even further to her grandmother where its grip was finally loosening.

"What do you want from me?" the girl demanded of the creature, staring deep into its black eyes.

The creature did not speak but instead showed her as a vision in her mind. She watched it curl itself upon a patch of skin heated by the sun. Not before long, however, the patch turned to ice with the presence of its cold body. So on it went, in search of another patch of warmth to heat its body.

She observed how this process had resulted in the winding of itself so tightly around her and her family—all from moving from one part to another, longing for a warm place to rest. It pulled tighter and tighter, stretching itself with sole focus upon its quest.

The girl felt its frantic search, its discomfort from the entanglement of its body, the fatigue from the constant moving and struggling. This creature was in pain, only trying to ease its suffering. "Who are you?" she questioned further.

Again, visions came to her instead of words. She witnessed a father abandoning his children with money in a briefcase. She saw a mother on her deathbed with her family nearby. Next a child, ashamed with the disapproval of her parents. Then, a baby being transferred into the arms of another. Flashes of images continued, and with each one, a visceral emotion came with it: anger, confusion, and betrayal.

Lastly, she was shown a female body—a body with a changing face. First the face was young, then middle aged, then very old. Something was peculiar about this changing face. On the outside, this woman wore a smile, yet her eyes showed a deep sadness held within. The girl gazed into these eyes and saw the woman crying. As her tears dropped to the floor, they morphed into this creature's body.

The girl understood now—this creature had been born from the suffering of her family, passed down through generations. The creature was not a malicious parasite but an entity simply searching for relief, comfort, and, ultimately, time in the light.

The girl's heart pulsed with empathy, and she felt the warmth of compassion radiate out across her body. The creature instantly reacted, constricting its body as if to absorb every bit of the girl's heat. The creature's dampness soaked into her skin, threatening to chill her to the bone. Its body felt like ice against her skin, and for a moment, the heat retreated as resentment took its place instead—resentment of the burden she had to bear.

Flashes of times where she felt unworthy and undeserving of affection streamed across her mind. She relived moments in her life where she felt drowned in her emotions, overwhelmed by everything she experienced. She recollected moments of regret and moments where she felt small or insignificant. Her life spun past her eyes, stopping at memories of guilt and shame; she felt the charge of these moments in her body as the creature squeezed her even tighter. Then, she remembered what it was searching for—the warmth of home.

The girl took a deep breath and recalled a memory that she held very dear in her heart—one so heavily guarded she never let anyone touch it, all to protect the preciousness of the moment and keep it safe inside. But now was not the time to hide—it was time to let this memory shine.

Suddenly, the girl was transported into the vision of this sacred memory. She remembered lying on her bed and felt the softness of the sheets. The sound of rain drummed on the roof, and thunder rattled the glass window. Another warm body quietly breathed next to her. Despite the chill of the outer world, she was warm and curled up to the one she loved with all her heart. Their love equally returned to her as he stroked her hair gently and hummed a mellow tune.

The noise of the storm drifted away, replaced by only the sound of their breath and hearts beating as one. Though the storm still raged on, here where she lay was as warm as a summer's day. She relived the warmth of their love like the sun beating down on her, sharing its love with the earth. In her own body, this sun and warmth was mirrored back to her beloved. She was at home here, nestled in the arms of someone who deeply cared.

She kept that image strong within her mind, radiating the bright golden light of the sun out into the space around her. Her whole body heated quickly, and finally she felt the creature relax its grip around her. She imagined herself beaming golden rays of light—her body was now a liquid sun, which she offered to this creature thirsty for love.

The girl whispered to the creature, "Take this and drink. May you always feel this warmth within your heart."

And so it did. The girl was no longer her body; she embodied the nourishment of life itself offering herself freely to this demon who haunted her family. As it feasted, its body slowly eased and then even began to shrink. Smaller and smaller this creature became—she saw her grandmother become free of its entanglement, and then it released her mother and then her. The creature grew smaller and smaller, transforming into a mere worm.

The girl bent down to pick up this tiny creature, no longer a fearsome foe but now one of the earth's greatest allies. The girl asked the creature again, "Who are you?"

And once more she received images: She saw this creature in its natural habitat, in the soil, moving inch by inch. As it went, it devoured that which was no longer in use, leaving behind rich and fertile nutrients.

The revelation struck the girl with purity and wisdom—the medicine of this creature as the cycle of compost, its role of transforming what no longer served into fuel that facilitated growth.

Akaal to Earth

The girl sat in deep meditation behind the wall. She could feel its ever-present boundary, even with her eyes closed, her awareness journeying into the depths of her consciousness. How long had she been trapped here? She would never forget the day that she heard the distress beacon call out from this place, offering eternal praise, worship, and reverence in exchange. Back then, it seemed so glorious, but she soon discovered that eternal was a very long time. The girl bit back the bitterness she felt within her bones, at the lure into this reality and betrayal of those who had dared call for help.

The girl opened her eyes reluctantly to her surroundings. A white alabaster wall stood directly in front of her as a semi translucent veil to the outside world. If she stood up against this pale barrier and looked beyond its confinement, she could see a long hallway on the other side, moving in both directions.

A radiant light graced her hallway, marking the part of the day the girl most looked forward to. The girl pressed her hands against the wall before her and peered down the hall to the left. Slowly the light she so longed to see flooded into the space. The source of this light was ultimately unknown to her—it was bright like starlight and gave warmth to the otherwise cold stone and sand that made up the other three walls of her captivity.

How she longed to touch and emerge into the light. It called to her like nothing before. This moment in time was her favorite, when the light beamed and playfully bounced off the white walls, illuminating the hallway along its way. The people would be coming soon; they always arrived shortly after the light danced its way through the hall.

The girl backed away from this translucent boundary and sat once more upon the sandy ground. She recalled when she first tried to break this veil of a wall. In the beginning, her bitterness often turned into rage. Using that rage, she would attempt to burst through and penetrate its hold. For a moment, it would shatter in her vision and then instantly reform within a blink of an eye.

Many times she tried this, but it would only stand firm once more no matter the amount of force she exerted. With many memories of defeat swirling in her mind, she closed her eyes and let herself sink inward—here she could escape her captivity within her dreams and spent many great lengths of time pushing her creative imagination to the brink. In this space within, she was free.

In her dreams, the girl swam in warm yet deep bodies of water, flew above stately mounds of earth reaching toward the sky, and ran effortlessly between wood pillars blooming with fresh flowers. Her body morphed at her desire, and every whim unfolded within a moment. This fluid realm of experience was the closest to her natural home; far and wide she traveled deep within the limitlessness of her mind. Was she awake or asleep? Maybe somewhere in between. Anything was possible here in this liminal space, revealed upon her will.

She rested here until the shuffling of feet echoed down the way. Her eyes fluttered open, watching carefully with anticipation the other side. Soon would come her offering, the exchange for her presence here, the promise of worship and praise. Humans in white robes finally came into view and placed their gifts upon the floor. It was then that they began to chant her favorite song—the tones and rhythm could not be ignored, for they invigorated her very essence; so deeply this melody moved her that she had no choice but to dance to its tune.

Many times, she tried to refuse this urge to dance but could not resist its ecstasy. The sound of their voices reverberated through her enclosure, and the light seemed to dance with it. Soon enough, she found herself upon her feet, twirling with her reverent song. Her body hummed in response, emanating her bliss out to them. She knew the people could feel it when their lips spread in gentle smiles as they sang.

It was in these moments that all bitterness she held for those who knelt on the floor before her slowly seeped away, no more resentment or feelings of betrayal present within her bones. Here in her dance and the people's song she felt them connect through the confines of the wall—this weaving of their union continued until all were aglow.

The chanted song of praise was coming to a close. The final note left their lips, and then came the silent stillness that reminded her of home. She stood there facing the wall, the echoes of vibration fading into the ever-present silence that always lay beneath the sound. Nothing existed in this moment but the bliss of OM.

Soon the shuffling would begin again, and the people would begin to rise. The girl looked longingly at the dispersing crowd, pressed her hands upon the wall, and cried. Tears of joy and sorrow alike flowed freely from her eyes. They saturated the ground beneath her feet and seeped into the sand, glittering briefly as if to say "goodbye."

The girl then caught his eye, the man on the other side—the only one who seemed to linger within her shrine. He was the only one who dared to look intently upon her wall. At first she thought he could see her, so she jumped and waved her arms, but no acknowledgment came that he had seen such a scene.

Once before he had dared to press his palm upon the wall when all others had departed. She mirrored him, placing her palm upon the wall. The man's eyes searched the wall for perhaps a response, until he finally closed them in prayer. The wall resonated with his plea for relief from the pain he held within his heart.

She held her hand there against his own, only the thin veil in between. She too closed her eyes, and only then did the visions unfold—visions of barren fields, laden with dust…visions of warm and friendly faces…a child's enthusiastic greeting at the door. The sorrow of suffering gripped her throat, and tears burst forth from her eyes without restraint. She released them freely to the earth and offered them to his prayer for rain.

In that moment—and for only a moment—the feeling of the wall disappeared. She could feel the warmth of his hand and the rough sensation of his hardened skin. A gentle smile bloomed upon his lips, and his soft-spoken words of "I see you" crossed the divide. Her fingers twitched as if to clasp his hand in hers, but it was at that point he released his hand from the wall, backed away, and bowed.

Today his eyes lingered upon the wall once more, yet there was something more held within them—a twinkle that shone as bright as her sacred light. As the others passed along their way, he approached the wall and again placed his hand upon it. She eagerly met him with her own. Closing her eyes, she saw the visions emerge within her awareness. This time, the fields were rich in green growth, sparkling with luminescent light reflected in its moisture.

She opened her eyes with a start to find the man staring back into her. Tears welled in his eyes, and he spoke once more through the divide: "Thank you for your tears." He removed his hand and bowed deeply, his forehead touching the floor. He stood, facing the white-golden light, and continued to the opening at the end of the hall with an expression of gratitude.

Stunned, the girl continued to stare as an idea blossomed within her mind: the boundaries of this room were not fully confined. The water she had offered to the ground seemed to seep through. The formless tears of her emotions traveled within the earth to the world beyond the wall.

Still her hand rested upon the glassy wall, yet she noticed the quality had shifted. She pushed against it with a mighty shove but found it only pushed her back. She relaxed with a breath and recalled the formless transparency of water. She felt her body loosen and become more spacious, vibrating like individual droplets of fine mist. Suddenly her hand went through, only to be gripped again within the wall in response to her surprise.

She closed her eyes, allowing the boundaries of her body to become once more like a fine mist. The wall relinquished its hold upon her, and she made her way through, body and all. The wall passing through her felt refreshing and cool.

Standing now for the first time in the hall, she felt a warmth brush itself upon her skin. She turned toward the source—toward her sacred light that had greeted her time and time again. The warmth sank deep within her skin. She followed the glow down the hallway and out through a large door; there she found the green fields from the man's visions laid out before her. Cresting upon the field's horizon, a great ball of light seemed to be ablaze with fire. She heard its tone ring true as it called out to her, "Welcome home."

With its grace upon her, she released her body to the wind and danced upon the breeze. Tears swelled within her eyes despite her permission.

She fell with them to the earth and soaked into its cool embrace, only to rise up in form, to once more greet this glorious star.

This bliss she carried with her time and time again, back to the shrine that once confined her. As the holy light traced the hallway she knew so very well, she greeted the people in their song with her ecstatic dance—there she shared her bliss and shed her tears freely.

Heartwood Memories

The girl was in a place she had never been to before, yet at the same time, it was all so very familiar, like a déjà vu. The lush-green grass beneath her bare feet compelled her to frolic and roll around like a child. However, before she had the chance to indulge, a beam of light shone directly into her eyes. It came down through a circular opening at the top of the cave, glinting off a pond with a gentle waterfall and rocky stream. The sun bounced off the surface, grabbing her attention, calling for her to look into its waters.

The cave was still and almost silent except for the quiet bubbling of the small waterfall. She knelt at the edge and peered into its depth. Expecting to see the bottom of a small body of water, she continued to stare, confused, into the crystal-clear waters. There was no bottom, just the gentle decreasing of light—bright and luminous at the top near the edges, fading into a dark and ominous tone near the center.

The girl swung her legs around and dropped her feet into the water. It was warm and welcoming. All of her tension flowed from her body, revealing itself as ripples dancing across the glassy surface. The warmth worked its way up her body, settling into her heart. The girl sighed with relief and the ease of relaxation.

A sudden giggle bubbled up inside her, and she wiggled her toes in delight, squishing the amorphous water between them. The echo of her laughter bounced along the cave walls, and everything seemed to glow brighter as it did. *Such a weird place,* the girl thought to herself. A place so spacious yet contained. The more the girl thought about this, the more her eyebrows furrowed at the center. The vibrancy seemed to dim as the girl became lost in her thoughts.

She let out a deep yawn, stretching her arms. It would be easy to fall asleep here, to rest with quiet ease. The girl lay down upon her back, legs still dangling over the edge into the water. Looking up above her, she noticed several tree branches hanging over into her field of view. The way the light danced through the leaves reminded the girl of a memory from long ago when she was a child—the memory of watching the sky and calling out the pictures she saw within the clouds; it was so long ago the girl questioned if the memory was real or simply just a dream.

The girl rolled onto her belly, her gaze following the branches to the trunk of a tree. A great oak tree stood there beckoning her into its presence. The wide, sturdy trunk even had a concave section near the ground, just big enough for the girl to nestle her body within it. She rested her back against the bark. The trunk of the tree wrapped around her body, holding her in its embrace. A deep breath and another sigh of relief—with the tree supporting her back, she felt like she could accomplish anything.

She peered upward, tracing the spreading branches with her eyes. They moved out from the center in all directions, like a neuron in the brain. Some branches went quite high, and others shot out long, creating space for her to climb, if she wished to do so. She scanned for lower branches, looking for a foothold, and there, just to her left side, was one low enough for her to pull herself up on.

Her inner child jumped up with glee. When was the last time she had climbed a tree? Another memory came rolling back, of climbing the crab apple tree in her backyard. She must have been only six or seven at the time. Another pang of memory came right after—the pain of falling out of that apple tree and the vow to never climb so high again.

What seemed high to her as a child didn't seem so grand now; the fear became a distant recollection of what once felt out of reach. With determination set in her eyes, she walked over to the oak's low-hanging branch. She wrapped her arms around it and lifted herself onto the ledge.

One foot at a time, she stood tall and reached for another, steadily climbing higher and higher. This was easy, no problem at all—until she looked beneath her and her heart beat even faster with the distant view of the ground below. *Calm, deep breaths,* the girl repeated to herself. As she breathed deeper, the tree encouraged her to climb higher by tickling her cheek with a stray leaf.

Higher she climbed, until she came to a branch thick enough for her to stand upon. From the trunk of the tree, she looked out to where it led. Following its path, she found herself standing directly over the water. What a view from up here, seeing the whole thing from above. Up here, for some reason, it seemed so much larger.

The sunlight shone right into the center, highlighting everything, from the hole at the top of the cave to just beneath the water, piercing the smooth, clear surface. She stared deeper into the water, her body pressing forward over the ledge. She gripped tightly to another branch above her to get a better view.

The light hitting the water did funny things to her vision; she was beginning to see shapes and figures on the surface. Swirling images became clearer as she continued to stare into this silky mirror. At first, she briefly saw herself leaning precariously over from the branch's edge, and then it shifted into something she had long forgotten.

She saw herself as a child, being tossed high into the sky. She remembered that feeling of flight, the sensation of the expansive view out to the horizon.

"One day," she told her father, who threw her into the air. "One day, I am going to fly."

He hugged her tightly as she fell into his arms and swung her around, all while laughing. "I believe you."

The image switched again; this time, it was not a memory but a vision of her with great wings flying high in the sky, almost touching the sun. The girl leaned out further still, her weight pressing into her hands; she craned her neck for a clearer view. Suddenly, a snap came from above her. Her weight released from the branch's hold. Her eyes snapped shut, and she knew she was falling—but if she held out her arms, it was that same feeling she experienced as a child—the feeling of flying.

Spirit Walker

The desert was still and motionless; both earth and sky were a dusty orange with only the thin line of horizon in between. A gentle drumming faded into the sound of a padded thumping upon the sand. The girl's hips swayed with every step of the elephant's movement beneath her; the natural curves of its neck held her close and connected. She felt the elephant's strong legs as an extension of her own. The shifting of her sacrum elongated her spine with ease and softness. She took comfort in this stability—swaying like a metronome, she felt time extend out before her.

A "hoot" above and to the left drew her attention upward. A brown owl slowly circled, following the pace of the elephant's stride, its wings as silent as the air around it. The girl could feel the ease of the owl's glide within her own shoulder blades. The girl extended her arms, mimicking the owl's wings and letting the sensation spread all the way to her fingertips. Her fingers ran through the air with the impression of silken water, caressing the fabric of space itself.

"I could stay here forever," she said aloud.

A hissing string of words came from beneath the elephant's belly where a white snake slithered carefully, weaving its way forward through the footsteps of the giant beast. The world was so quiet the girl could hear the reply clearly: "Thisss isss not the final dessstinationnn."

"But it could be," the girl replied, lying her body down, resting on the topside of the elephant's back.

"You would not like it here," said the elephant, flapping its ears back. "This is merely the in-between."

As if on cue, the girl heard the ting of a small bell radiate down from the sky above. The vibration sent a pulse through her vision, causing the world around her to ripple. She sat up attentively as a section up ahead leaked like oil on water, becoming a prismatic and indistinct surface. Blurry images and splashes of color slowly formed within it. The girl rapidly blinked her eyes to make sure this was not simply a mirage of the desert. She watched as the images morphed into several cloudy sceneries before settling on one that resembled a bright-green and lush forest next to a tepid stream.

On the other side of this wavering screen, the girl watched carefully as a figure walked out from the woods and came to the edge of the preci-pice—there it stopped and waited. The figure's presence elicited a feeling of recognition but one the girl couldn't place. The girl gently patted the elephant, offering her thanks through touch alone. She slid off from its back and walked to this effervescent partition, positioning herself to match the figure on the other side and looked at it with curiosity. Behind her, she felt the elephant step in close to her back. Simultaneously the owl gently landed on the girl's left shoulder, and a slithering constriction on her right arm informed her the snake was also with her.

The fuzzy image in front of her showed a figure of similar build and gender but with skin much lighter and hair much darker and shorter. Its face was obscured by the sheen and shimmer of the translucent wall. The girl slowly raised her hand. The reflection on the other side also moved, matching the gesture as a mirrored action. As the girl's fin-gertips brushed the very edge of this strange barrier, its texture shifted rapidly to that of a torrential waterfall. Pushing her hand in further, she connected with another hand from the other side. It was soft and tender. As their palms touched, an electric current ran through the girl's spine, causing all the hairs on her body to rise to attention.

The owl tilted its head playfully in anticipation and voiced with a purring trill, "When the call of the bell is answered, another self shall be revealed." The hand from the other side tightened its grip around her and pulled.

The Sensitive One

There she was, the sensitive one. The girl peered into the darkness pierced by a bright beam of light, spotlighting a younger version of herself cowering in a tight ball—this was the sensitive part of herself, the one who felt everything. The girl walked closer, with an even and soft-footed step, nothing too forthcoming or abrupt. The girl could feel herself in this other image, the tightness of her body braced against the intensity of her experience.

The girl stopped when she reached a clear cylindrical wall made of what seemed to be bulletproof glass surrounding this small self. She placed one hand up to it. The wall vibrated with unseen sonic waves, bouncing and shaking as if a part of a speaker. The girl could feel herself on the other side being pulverized by the sound of booming voices beating down upon her.

If only this part of herself could hear her. The girl tried shouting, banging on the wall, jumping up and down, and waving her arms, but the small figure was so tucked into herself that nothing got through. A tsunami of sensation was tearing through this enclosure; her eyes clenched shut, fighting the torrent of tears, her hands cupping her ears in a futile attempt to stop the onslaught of noise.

How lost this part of her felt, and she could hear the internal questioning: "Where am I? How did I get here?" and an ever-present sense of "I don't want to be here." The girl's heart broke with empathy. Her small self was right there, just on the other side of the wall—so close yet so very far away.

She wanted nothing more than to cradle this part of herself, to soothe her tension and help ease her suffering. *But how do I reach her? How do I reach her when she is locked up so tightly within herself?* The girl sat down, and there she waited patiently—there had to be a moment eventually where she could be heard.

The girl waited for a very long time—and, yes, there were moments when the figure inside stopped crying or cautiously released her ears. The girl seized those moments to tell this version of herself how much she really cared, but the only responses were "I don't believe you" and "You're not real." Then her small self would curl back into a ball, blocking out the world around her—so bombarded with noise, overwhelmed by her surroundings, it was truly difficult to reach her.

Time passed by, and not once did the girl abandon her post. She tried sending messages through animals and flowers; she offered ways to mediate the noise and shade her from the bright, piercing light, none of which lasted very long. What she was feeling was only being suppressed, and it came back with a roar that blasted through any barrier in its way. Her small self huddled on the edge, absorbing it all.

The girl cried for this part of herself. Did she not realize how strong she was, to have survived this long without dissolving into nothingness? Day after day, she braced against it all, fighting the urge to simply wither away and perish. So what was she holding on to that kept her alive? The girl closed her eyes, feeling with her senses through the barrier, reaching out with her heart to understand what was being protected so deeply within this creature. There in her mind unfolded an image—a mother rocking her baby and singing a lullaby.

The girl felt her yearning, desperately clinging to a mother's love. And so she began to sing the lullaby. With every note, she offered the message to her younger self: "The love you seek is right here; you only have to receive it. I am right here." She sang, and she sang, never once giving up, waiting patiently for the day when her inner child would hear her.

Dance of the Dragon

This must be a dream, the girl thought. *I was just lying down for a moment, to rest from this inner strife. Then suddenly I'm here.* The girl faced a dark cavern flickering with a gentle glow. A shadow bounced from wall to wall with groans of madness echoing in the distance. The girl approached closer, moving around the shadowed bend to a larger cave opening.

Slowly she peeked her head around the corner and saw a most frightful sight: a little red dragon spewing fire all around, climbing up to the ceiling, and then beating on the walls. Screams of fire circled the little beast, engulfing it in an inferno. *What is this place? It looks like hell.* The girl's heart ached for the little beast who seemed trapped in its own thoughts. Suddenly, the girl's hand slipped, and a small rock went skittering across the floor.

The little dragon snapped its head around, its eyes glaring toward the sound. "Who goes there?" it yelled with a mighty roar. "Who dares enter here?"

The girl pressed her back along the wall, breathing heavy breaths. *This really must be a dream—how did I get here?* The girl ran through her memory of what exactly she was thinking when she laid her head to rest. Ah, it was coming back now—the frustration and anger of what her mother had said. Her heart had been burning with the pointed words, leaving an ache in her chest. How she longed to talk to this anger she felt, to understand what it needed, for she just couldn't bear to let it out.

She could feel the tiny beast walking softly to the edge of its enclosure when it stopped abruptly and let a stream of fire out through the opening. The girl felt the heat brush her skin, burning with the pain she felt within. She knew this feeling well—the desire to set ablaze anything that deemed itself worthy to enter her personal space. She could relate with this red dragon hurling fire left and right, no matter who was in the way.

"I just want to talk!" she exclaimed around the corner and then waited patiently for an answer.

"Show yourself!" the beast responded. "If you have the courage."

That is a very good question, the girl thought. *Do I have the courage to face this beast of rage?* She could hear the dragon tiring, breathing harder with every released flame. *This is why I am here,* the girl resolved, *to face my anger.* She then stepped around the corner with a final exhalation, ready to meet what was there in waiting. She turned into the entrance and walked into the cave of flames.

"You!" the dragon roared, eyes narrowing at her approach. "How dare you come here!"

The girl looked into the eyes of this angry beast and saw a flash of something she recognized—the anguished face of someone wrestling with a pain that weighed heavily on their heart. They stared into each other's eyes, she and this beast, with not a word exchanged; only this silent resonance of empathy stirred the air around them while their shadows danced along the walls.

A wave of sorrow rippled through the girl as she remembered the rejection and shame. She could hear her mother's spear-tongued words and feel how they hit her with such vigor. She remembered the vicious impulse to retaliate but instead vowed to lock away that which demanded to act out.

As if the little beast sat there with remembrance too, it turned its back to the girl and over its shoulder simply stated, "You were supposed to protect me, yet you trapped me in this cage. I only wanted to be heard. Why did you put me here instead?"

The girl took a step closer to the dragon and reached out her hand. It snapped its head away and became suddenly enraged; once more, it began its dance of flames and pounding against the walls, roaring into the space. The girl could feel its agony as if the beast was her own soul—a numb chill in the depth of its core no matter how hot the fires roared.

"I'm sorry," she said in little more than a whisper. "I didn't know what to do."

As if driven by madness, the crazed dragon kept reeling until suddenly it stopped and collapsed upon the floor, still panting. It tried to stand, but its body shook now. Slowly the redness of its body faded to purple and then went blue. It curled into a tight little ball and wept—it was a quiet weeping hidden under the crackling of flames. And there it shook and shivered, looking so small.

Again the girl saw herself embedded in this dragon. The girl took another step forward, watching closely for its reaction, but the dragon barely opened its eyes, which were heavy with exhaustion. Carefully she continued forward to the center of the cave and softly sat upon the floor next to this little beast. As gently as she would pet a cat, she ran her hand along the dragon's back. At first, the dragon stiffened and then relaxed into the touch.

Her next words came with a depth of understanding. "I am sorry I put you in here; I wanted to protect myself from the pain. I was so scared what would happen if I let you out. I wanted to protect *our family* from *me*."

A sudden burst of tears came streaming down the girl's face, with heaving sobs she had never before let out. The little dragon then nestled closer, nuzzling its face against the girl's leg—they huddled there together until the flames subsided.

The little dragon then raised its head, faced the girl, and pleaded, "I promise I won't cause trouble if you let me speak another way about this pain that I am feeling. I don't like being locked away. It's hot on the outside yet so cold on the inside. No matter how much I spew fire, there's an ache in my chest wanting to come out, to disengage. I need relief from this pain—I need a way out of this place. Please help. Make it go away. Protect me from this pain; protect me from this hurt. I don't want to feel it anymore. I just want to create and play."

The girl watched as the dragon spoke, its scales falling away. One by one, they tumbled from its skin, revealing her own reflection. They stared into one another's eyes, and the girl felt her lips move effortlessly with the words: "Thank you. I love you. I'm sorry. Please forgive me." The mirrored image of herself smiled and then slowly faded.

Record Keeper

The girl closed the book. *Hmph! What a boring ending—no intrigue, no conclusion, just a tale that ceased to exist with unfinished business.* Not all books ended in quite a lackluster way such as this one, though—there were plenty others she could read. The girl glanced down the long hallway. Shelves extended out as far as the eye could see, each one at least twelve feet tall, stacked from end to end.

The girl took the heavy book from the stand she had been reading it upon and walked to a nearby shelf. The book held quite some weight to it, for it was a long life lived. The soft, yet sturdy cover always brought a tactile pleasure to the girl as she ran her finger mindlessly along the spine. The golden title shimmered with a soft glow from the lights above. In the missing slot upon the closest shelf, she slid this book back into place with an audible sigh.

The Library was her favorite place, and she was honored to call it home. The quiet space brought her much comfort—this was the place of All-Knowing, a place where you could find the answer to any question you may have. The girl continued down the long corridor, gracefully trailing her fingertips across the exposed spines as she replayed moments of the story she had so recently finished.

She wondered why the protagonist couldn't express his feelings to the one woman who actually saw him for who he was. He just surrendered all desires to pursue success in his business. He became a rich man with much authority in his world but died alone with a weighted heart—there was still so much he could give.

The girl's heart felt twisted with empathetic pains for this man's suffering. It could have been such a different ending, more like the stories she loved to read most: the tales of the heroes standing up for what they believe despite the odds of defeat, the ones of true love and freedom.

"You look troubled."

The girl looked up to see an older man descending a ladder, resting upon a bookcase. His kind eyes crinkled behind his small round glasses.

"I can't stand it when the story ends with..." She waved her hands in the air, exasperated. "Nothing!" She continued under her breath, "You call that living? Seems like such a waste."

The older man's long gray beard bobbled with his chuckle. "Not all stories are ones with happy endings. As much as we see the bigger picture of one's tale, it is not always so clear from their perspective." He paused. "Do you know why we keep records of every life lived?"

"Because their story is sacred, no matter how it unfolds."

"Yes, that's right! And?"

"And each holds a valuable lesson of life itself." The girl recited the ethos of her kind: the Record Keepers.

"Yes!" The older man's voice boomed. "The fragments of creation, my dear! It is our duty and responsibility to protect them." He looked down at the girl over the rim of his glasses. "And treat them with care," he finished, with pointed words.

They continued to walk together in silence.

"Ah, here we go!" The man beelined to the closest shelf. The books on this shelf looked more tattered and worn. He took a maroon book off the shelf; the golden name glittered as he handed it to the girl. "This one I think you should read next. You might be surprised," he said with a wink.

The girl took the book reluctantly.

The older man shouted over his shoulder as he strode away, "Come find me after and tell me if you still feel the same."

The girl looked around her, searching for an available reading stand. There was one a few rows back, next to the window emanating a soft yellow light—ideal for reading. She plopped the heavy book on the slender podium. The name of the book was almost illegible. The writing was visibly worn despite the preservation methods here at the Library.

Some stories here were considered "Great," like those of Jesus, Buddha, Mozart, da Vinci, and even Shakespeare. Their books were read by many and kept well preserved with so many eyes watching for wear. Yet there were many, many books here in the Library, ones that were hardly read—these could easily become overlooked, and therefore the wear upon them was less noticeable.

The girl opened the book and settled into a flow, slowly unfolding this soul's tale. At first, it started no different than any other life—normal, if there was such a thing. A plain story of a shepherd boy searching for his purpose and truth. Yet once the girl started the story, she could not stop. On she read, well into the evening. Even when others slowly put their books back and headed to their private quarters, she still continued.

Everywhere this shepherd traveled, he met people with such selfless acts of compassion and kindness that the impact of his presence changed their course in a moment. One he crossed paths with was a "Great" soul on his own journey to finding truth. Their interaction was simple and pure, yet she wondered if he had not interacted, would this "Great" have ever found their fate? Their meeting was as gentle as a butterfly landing on a flower, yet so much shifted in their greeting.

It was starting to approach first light, and still the girl read on. She had to know how this life unfolded, how this soul met his end. At one point in the story, this shepherd came to a crossroad, metaphorically speaking. Either he could continue traveling with his flock or choose to court a girl he was keen on. He chose to settle down and live a simple life with his now wife and eventually family. He was content with what he had and pursued nothing more—there he died with three generations by his side.

The girl slowly closed the book and cradled it in her arms, his last words echoing in her mind: *Thank you for the memories.*

A voice startled her out of her thought stream. "Ah! I see you have finished." The old man approached her from the left, walking down the hall, and put a hand upon her shoulder. "Quite quickly, I might add. So, what do you think?"

"I am confused," the girl began. "He could have easily become one of these 'Great' souls that everyone knows, yet no one really knew how much he changed the world around him. No one recognized him—an unsung hero."

"Ahh, but is that really true? His family who surrounded him knew just how special he was."

The girl bowed her head, running the story through her mind again.

The old man lifted her chin and looked her in the eye. "What if I told you this was the same soul of the story you so recently read? The one you were so disappointed in. What would you say then?"

The girl raised her eyebrows in surprise and then furrowed them together. "How is that possible?" the girl replied.

"You know very well that time is not linear—this soul's heart was torn upon reentry. He desired greatness but could not decide whether this was to be great love or great change upon the world. So he chose to experience both, and as you can see, there are echoes of each in the other."

The girl nodded in agreement—both held lessons of the pursuit of happiness and commitment to his chosen path.

The old man continued, "This story may not be considered 'Great,' yet it is important all the same."

The girl held the book tightly to her chest and gave it a squeeze, like an old friend. "I think I should take this down to the preservation hall; it could use some upkeep."

The old man smiled. "I would agree."

The girl spun on her heels and skipped down the hall.

Snowy Reveries

The tea cycled through the girl's body, warming her to her core. She melted into the thickly upholstered cushion and rested her back along the carpeted wall. A calmness swept through her surroundings. The quiet clink of tea cups and the soft murmurs of others nearby filled the teahouse—it was an especially quiet morning. The snow falling outside had encouraged most of the regulars to remain home today. No one here was in a rush to finish their tea or in a rush to leave its warmth.

The girl gazed outside the window. The gentle blue glow of the snow illuminated the landscape. Trees slowly gathered snow upon their branches with fanned-out arms of pine needles. Not a creature stirred except for the occasional flapping of a bird moving from one roosting spot to the next. As she stared into the dancing snow, it seemed to be giving her a private show. She watched as the flakes twirled, and she couldn't, even if she tried, remember a sight more beautiful than this one here.

A sigh of relief escaped her—this was her time to be and nothing more; she was a quiet observer to the beauty that held her so tenderly. There was no pulling or pushing, just contentment to be right where she was; no need or desire clung to her mind, begging her to consider. No one poked at her with small talk or chatter. *Ah yes, the beauty of simplicity,* the girl thought as she smiled.

The steam from her cup warmed her face as she brought it up toward her lips. The aroma stirred a memory within her—a time of innocence and purity. Though this memory was not of this lifetime, she mused at where it must have come from. A simpler time perhaps, when the world was less busy and there was more time to just *be*.

As if the few sharing this environment with her were having the same fantasy, a hush fell over the place. The girl's imagination grew and blossomed within her mind's eye. She was here and there all at the same time. The trees outside were no longer evergreens but bamboo. The teahouse—no more simply so—became an ornate temple with a steepled roof. Red and gold decorated the interior, and she swore she could hear a bell ringing.

This image and feeling overlaid her every sensation. She could still feel the cushion underneath her, but she could also explore this other world she had never been to before. She began to remember a time beyond the veil of her immediate reality.

It was then the obscuration lifted, and the dream she had touched became crystal clear. Any distinction of her environment did not matter to her, nor did the question of the past or future, as she was taken in so fully by the feeling.

Yes, she existed now in a space where her presence was absolutely celebrated—everything around her was alive; the air made way for her body. Nature rustled with joyous greetings. The floor held firm as if to say, "I've got you." The rays of the sun caressed her face. The whole universe wrapped around her, cradling her in its arms. It rocked her spirit as gently as a mother would a babe.

A mere whisper reached her ears, something she couldn't quite hear. *Come again?* The girl replied in her mind. More words came through louder, though still as if underwater. The girl silently called to the wisdom that longed to reach her. The words then finally rang true within her ear: "Miss? Sorry to bother you, but would you like another cup of tea?"

The girl, shaken from her reverie, found herself once more seated upon the teahouse floor. A young girl looked at her, waiting patiently for the answer to her question that was still hanging in the air. With a gentle smile, the girl replied, "Oh, yes, please."

Radiance

She was dissolving—the girl could no longer feel her body. The boundaries of it expanded out beyond where she could physically reach, uninhibited by its density. *If I dissolve, then am I still me?* she wondered as the confines and limitations she had beholden to herself began to slip away.

The light that illuminated her heart had only just started small, like that of a candle flame. Yet as she had drawn her breath into her center, the flame had grown into a massive pillar. This pillar of light touched both the heavens above her and the far depths of the earth below her. A bridge that she sat so rooted upon and alight in every way, it pulled at the shadows clinging onto her, desperately using her body as a shield.

She could feel them squirming upon her, searching for respite, all to avoid facing this bright, all-encompassing light. Yet even so she continued to breathe; the pillar was ever expanding in all directions—this was when her body had begun to shift and fade. With little to grasp on to, the shadows had no choice but to be revealed—and where there was light, no shadow could conceal itself.

Unable to withstand such a torrent of illumination, their screams of woe echoed in her ears as they lured her to remember what they represented: her guilt, her regret, her shame, and her grief. The girl wondered, *If I were to let go of all this, would I still continue to exist?*

On it went, growing ever brighter and wider with every deeply drawn breath, until she felt this pillar reach the sun at the very center of the solar system. All of time spread out before her; all paths taken and not taken encircled her awareness, branching out in all directions to the past, future, and present.

It was all so very strange, yet oddly familiar, like she had been here many, many times before. Overwhelmed by such an influx of information, the girl could not understand such vastness. The light penetrated her, urging her to release all control and all futile attempts to comprehend; yet she felt her body constrict with hesitation. *If I surrender, will I forget where I am?*

This internal debate lasted for quite some time—or it could have been a mere moment. A second stretched into an hour, but perhaps it was the opposite—an hour compressed into a second. Through this inner dialogue, an illumination of truth began to shine through. Even as her body's tangibility faded, she noticed she still held consciousness but of a different nature.

One by one, her fingers dissolved, yet the energy of them did not disappear; instead, they morphed with the greatness of space. Next began her legs and arms, and like a snake shedding its skin, she expanded out of her shell to bask in this radiant light.

An intrigue dawned upon the girl, and she pondered with delight, *If I release the parameters of my body, just how big can I be?* As instantly as her question touched her mind, all form she knew collapsed, and she expanded her inner self out to all eternity.

Emanating out in all of space and time, she allowed herself to shine brighter and more fiercely. No longer was the sun above her—no, she had grown so large and grand that the sun was now residing in her very center. The fluidity of her energy rippled with every emotion, and still the fire that burned within held firm and stable. Everything made sense now—her purpose, her calling, her true self, and her nature.

Feeling lost was no matter, for the mirror of illusion had shattered. From nothing to no thing, the radiance of this light became her, for that is who she was and ever will be.

Epilogue: Nowhere to Now Here

The girl found herself in a large white marbled hall. Grand pillars surrounding the girl rose up to a ceiling so high that it was difficult to decipher whether it had a ceiling at all or simply merged into the clouds above her. The light was gentle and softly reflected off the marble like dawn's first light touching the night sky.

The smooth floor felt cool upon her bare feet. The girl walked further into the space ahead, moving past a large arched doorway, and found herself in front of the most beautiful fountain. Upon the floor, there was a large circular pool and another smaller circular basin resting upon a pillar, coming up from a small island in the center—all carved out of the same white marble. Stone slabs acted as a pathway through the circular pool that led to the center platform.

The girl walked quietly and gently, each step carefully considered and taken with much presence. The sanctity of this place demanded such manners from her—this was a place to hold sacred. With each step, she felt the bottom of her foot meet the floor beneath it, heel to toe, heel to toe, without making a sound. Each step made with the reverence of a sanctuary.

The girl made her way up to the basin, which she saw also held water—water so clear and still it created the perfect reflection. With an unconscious impulse, she moved her hand up and held it out over the water, feeling called to touch it with her finger.

She hovered her finger just above the glass-like surface, yet before she was able to move any further, a voice from behind startled her: "Here you are again, my child. Welcome back."

The girl turned around to meet a luminescent creature with great white feathered wings—an angel, a real angel. Stunned, the girl stared and then stuttered, unsure, "I...I...I'm sorry, have we met before?"

The angel returned a gentle smile. "Yes, dear; although you may not remember it now, I have greeted you every time you have journeyed here." The angel then made her way toward the girl and joined her on the island. Her movements were smooth and seamless—in the same way the girl walked in this place, the angel walked with equal grace.

As she stepped upon the marble platform, the waters around the girl glowed with the same soft light illuminating the walls around her. The girl gazed into the large pool surrounding her. Within the reflective waters, snippets of her life appeared, shimmering in and out of focus. The longer she stared, the more they transformed into scenes that felt like distant dreams—but, yes, she could confidently say they were memories. Although whether they were past, present, or future, she could not decipher. The boundaries of time felt blurry, like the thin veil between each moment of time—each second, minute, hour, day, week, month, and year all merged into the sense of happening all at once.

The angel placed a hand upon her shoulder as the girl attempted to wrap her head around such a conundrum of logistics and reality. She spoke to recall the girl's attention. "This is your Hall of Remembering, your soul's reflection. Come—let me show you." The angel motioned toward the standing basin in the middle of the marble platform and guided the girl to look once more upon the watery reflection. "Look closely and see."

The girl let her eyes drift to the glassy surface, and like the images in the pool just before, she watched memories of her life appear.

The angel spoke. "You have wrestled with anger." A dark cave charred with fire appeared in the water. "Danced with liberation," the angel continued. The girl watched as people spun all around her, and she, too, remembered the twirling. The angel kept speaking: "And surrendered to sadness." A rainy landscape revealed itself then, and the girl lifted her hand to her cheek as she felt the coolness of the raindrops upon it.

The angel then guided the girl to look into her eyes. They were dark yet luminescent, highly contrasted by the white marble walls and feathered wings. There was a depth to them like a great void with awareness staring back at her from beneath their surface. The angel's voice rang inside her head, yet no words were spoken from her lips. "It is time to choose which journey you seek next. Close your eyes, and sense the path you must take."

The girl obeyed and brought her attention to her feet. The marble floor warmed beneath them. She recalled the quiet energy of walking through the great hall and the peace she felt within her heart. The crown of her head began to buzz and tingle. A great vortex of energy swirled above her, and still her body remained in tranquil silence. The girl's heart pulsed forward, guiding her to take a step.

The simplicity of walking engulfed her awareness. She saw herself, as if watching from above, choosing her steps with great clarity and tenderness. Her feet were patient, only ready to move when called to. Her heart, confident, was sure that her feet would find the floor. Her gaze merged into the inner depths of the darkness beyond her closed eyes—they were focused, unfazed by any distractions.

As if transported into the dark void, the girl walked forward, one step at a time. Where her heart tugged her, she turned, following its pulse like true north. Unseen ripples billowed out around her; the threads of fate itself began to weave the fabric of reality all around her. She did not need to see in this space, for although it was pitch-black, she was not truly blind. An inner light burned within her like sonar emanating out into the world around her, helping her navigate like a fish following the unseen current of a stream.

While the world around her was largely unknown, she felt safe in the depths of her womb. She felt the protection of the Great Holy Mother of life itself all around, encasing her with gentleness and compassion. Yes, a womb—that was where she was. Her body felt buoyant and light. The waters of life caressed her skin, and she hummed with the intensity of the entire cosmos within her, with the all-encompassing potential of creation itself. The girl's world split in her mind. She simultaneously rested in the womb of creation while also feeling the creative pulse within her own womb.

The pulsing in her body grew louder and louder until it resounded all around her. It vibrated the fluid essence that held her in suspension. Her own heart echoed with the heartbeat of the world around her. She understood then that the creator gives birth to creation...which then becomes the creator. *I am creation. I am that; I am.*

To be continued...

About Deysi Faeth

Deysi Faeth, a self-taught writer, beckons readers to explore the profound depths of human experience and the soul's mysteries. With a pen dipped in poetry and a visionary spirit, Deysi crafts intricate tapestries of short stories, poetry, and prose. Drawing inspiration from dream-work, mysticism, shamanism, and more, Deysi's work becomes an imaginative portal to explore life's mandala.

Deysi began her journey with open mic nights and literary magazines where she shared her art with the community. A true wordsmith, her unique perspective and evocative prose captured the hearts of those who ventured into her world of storytelling.

In her most recent collection, *Fragments of Creation*, Deysi unveils a tapestry woven from the threads of dreams, shamanic journeys, and parts integration practices. This work is more than a book; it is an offering—a sacred space for soul remembering, where the fragments of the self come together to create a harmonious whole.

Join Deysi Faeth on her literary odyssey, where each word is a brushstroke on the canvas of imagination, and every story is an exploration of the human spirit. Discover more about her offerings and artistry at DeysiFaeth.com.